Developing S~i
DEVELOPING SCIENTIFIC SKILLS AN

year

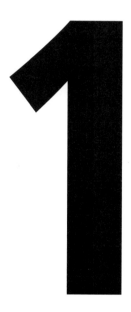

Christine Moorcroft

A & C BLACK

Contents

Reprinted 2004
Published 2003 by A & C Black Publishers Limited
37 Soho Square, London W1D 3QZ
www.acblack.com

ISBN 0-7136-6640-4

Copyright text © Christine Moorcroft, 2003
Copyright illustrations © Gaynor Berry, 2003
Copyright cover illustration © Kay Widdowson, 2003
Editor: Jane Klima
Design: Susan McIntyre

The author and publishers would like to thank Catherine Yemm,
Trevor Davies and the staff of Balsall Common Primary School
for their assistance in producing this series of books.

A CIP catalogue record for this book is available from the
British Library.

Printed in Great Britain by St Edmundsbury Press Ltd,
Bury St Edmunds, Suffolk.

A & C Black uses paper produced with elemental chlorine-
free pulp, harvested from managed sustainable forests.

Introduction

Developing Science is a series of seven photocopiable activity books for science lessons. Each book provides a range of activities that not only develop children's knowledge and understanding of science, but also provide opportunities to develop their scientific skills: planning experimental work, and obtaining and considering evidence.

The activities vary in their approach: some are based on first-hand observation, some present the findings of investigations for the children to analyse and others require the children to find information from books and electronic sources. They focus on different parts of a scientific investigation: questioning, responding to questions, generating ideas, planning, predicting, carrying out a fair test or an investigation, recording findings, checking and questioning findings, explaining findings and presenting explanations.

The activities in **Year 1** are based on Science in the National Curriculum and the QCA scheme of work for Year 1. They provide opportunities for the children to:
- develop curiosity about the things they observe and experience, and explore the world about them with all their senses;
- use this experience to develop their understanding of key scientific ideas and make links between different phenomena and experiences;
- begin to think about models to represent things they cannot directly experience;
- try to make sense of phenomena, seeking explanations and thinking critically about claims and ideas;
- acquire and refine the practical skills needed to investigate questions safely;
- develop skills of predicting, asking questions, making inferences, concluding and evaluating (based on evidence and understanding), and use these skills in investigative work;
- practise mathematical skills such as counting, ordering numbers, measuring using standard and non-standard measures and recording and interpreting charts;
- learn why numerical and mathematical skills are useful and helpful to understanding;
- think creatively about science and enjoy trying to make sense of phenomena;
- develop language skills through talking about their work and presenting their own ideas, using systematic writing of different kinds;
- use scientific and mathematical language (including technical vocabulary and conventions) and draw pictures, diagrams and charts to communicate scientific ideas;
- read non-fiction and extract information from sources such as reference books or CD-ROMs;
- work with others, respecting their ideas;
- develop respect for evidence and evaluate critically ideas which may or may not fit the evidence available;
- develop a respect for the environment and living things and for their own health and safety.

The activities are carefully linked with the National Literacy Strategy to give the children opportunities to develop their reading skills in finding information (for example, scanning a text, reading instructions and making notes) and to use a range of writing skills in presenting their findings (for example, labelling diagrams and writing simple reports). Links with literacy work and science-related vocabulary to be introduced are given in the **Notes on the activities** on pages 5–11.

Teachers are encouraged to introduce the activities presented in this book in a stimulating classroom environment that provides facilities for the children to explore, through play, using movement and the senses. For example, you could provide an activity corner where the children can investigate materials, equipment, pictures and books connected with the topics to be covered (such as magnets and different materials), or you could use role play or PE lessons to explore movements (such as the ways different animals move).

Each activity sheet specifies the learning outcome and has a **Teachers' note** at the foot of the page. Expanded teaching notes are provided in the **Notes on the activities**. Most activity sheets also end with a challenge (**Now try this!**) that reinforces the children's learning and provides the teacher with an opportunity for assessment. These activities might be appropriate for only a few children; it is not expected that the whole class should complete them. The extension activities should be completed in a notebook or on a separate sheet of paper.

Health and safety

Developing Science recognises the importance of safety in science lessons and provides advice on the ways in which teachers can make their lessons as safe as possible (including links to useful websites). The books also suggest ways in which to encourage children to take appropriate responsibility for their own safety. Teachers are recommended to follow the safety guidelines provided in the QCA scheme of work or in *Be Safe!* (available from the Association for Science Education). Specific health and safety advice is included in the **Notes on the activities** and warnings to the children feature on the activity sheets where relevant.

Online resources

In addition to the photocopiable activity sheets in this book, a collection of online science resources is available on the A & C Black website at www.acblack.com/developingscience. These activities can be used either as stand-alone teaching resources or in conjunction with the printed sheets. An icon on an activity page indicates that there is a resource on the website specifically designed to complement that activity.

To enable them to be used by children of a wide range of abilities, all of the activities on the website feature both written and spoken instructions. The tasks have been designed to provide experiences that are not easy to reproduce in the classroom: for example, children can investigate different sounds, see a video clip showing how an animal moves, or closely examine colour photographs of plants and flowers.

Notes on the activities

The notes below expand upon those provided at the foot of the activity pages. They give ideas and suggestions for making the most of the activity sheet, including suggestions for the whole-class introduction and the plenary session or for follow-up work using an adapted version of the activity sheet. To help teachers to select appropriate learning experiences for their pupils, the activities are grouped into sections within each book, but the pages need not be presented in the order in which they appear unless otherwise stated.

Ourselves

Many activities in this section can be introduced using songs from *Me* by Ana Sanderson (A & C Black), which includes songs about parts of the body, the senses, food and drink, and growth and change.

To prepare for **Body jigsaw** (page 12) the children could draw life-size body outlines and, in an ICT lesson, make large labels. The pictures could be made by groups of children, who could draw round the outline of one of the group  and then glue the labels onto different parts. This prepares for later work on movement, where the children name the parts of the body they move when performing different actions. This sheet also provides an opportunity for the children to write labels and to use labelled diagrams.

> **Vocabulary:** *ankle, elbow, forehead, hip, knee, neck, toe, wrist.*

Sense it (page 13) focuses on the ways in which we use our senses to find out about things. You could set up a 'feely box' and a 'smelly box' whose contents are changed each day. Also make sound recordings of familiar sounds and take photographs of the objects that make them: the children can hold up or point to the photograph that matches the sound being played, and say the word for the object (and the sound, if they can). You could have fun with *The Smelly Book* by Babette Cole (Collins Picture Lions). This page offers the children a chance to extend their vocabulary.

 Tasting should be carried out separately from other activities, using clean utensils (and the children should be made aware of these hygiene precautions).
The children should first wash their hands.
Warn them not to taste or smell unknown substances unless given to them by an adult they know and trust.

> **Vocabulary:** *ears, eyes, hands, hearing, mouth, nose, sight, skin, smell, taste, tongue, touch.*

Is it an animal? (page 14) discusses the essential characteristics of animals: they breathe, eat, drink and can move around (they also reproduce and excrete). Encourage the children to talk about familiar animals, such as their pets and any animals observed in the school grounds or on visits to zoos, farms, parks and so on. Ask them what they have seen the animals doing. Record their responses: you could group words that are connected with the same activity, such as moving, eating and drinking. They might have pets that have given birth to young: you could record the words the children use and introduce others. This page helps to extend the children's vocabulary.

> **Vocabulary:** *animal, birth, breathe, drink, eat, egg, lay, move, plant.*

A growing family (page 15) focuses on the ways in which people change as they grow older: they grow bigger, some parts of their bodies grow more than others; they change in other ways (for example, their hair might become grey, their skin might become wrinkled). The children could bring in photographs of themselves and other members of their families at different ages. Encourage them to talk about the changes they notice. Ask the children if people keep on growing bigger as they get older: you could introduce the idea that older people are not always taller than younger ones (this idea is developed on page 18). In this activity, the children have a chance to read and write captions.

> **Vocabulary:** *bigger, change, fatter, grow, smaller, taller, thinner.*

Happy Families: 1 and **2** (pages 16–17) encourage children to make observations of the differences between young and adult animals of the same species. The children could bring in photographs of their pets when they were young and as adults; invite them to show the class their photographs and talk about 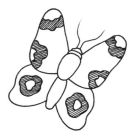 the ways in which their pets have changed. Talk about the changes in the lives of the animals depicted; introduce other stages that are not shown: for example, egg, pupa, spawn. Introduce the names of animals that might not be familiar to the children, such as *kid* and *owlet*. You could also make sets of cards for the children to play matching pairs. These pages offer the opportunity to extend the children's vocabulary.

> **Vocabulary:** *adult, butterfly, calf, cat, caterpillar, chick, cow, cub, dog, duck, duckling, egg, foal, frog, frogspawn, goat, hen, horse, kid, kitten, lamb, lion, owl, owlet, pig, piglet, puppy, sheep, tadpole, tiger.*

From shortest to tallest (page 18) could be introduced through reading the story *Once There Were Giants* by Martin Waddell (Walker Books), which shows a baby girl among the 'giants' (the adults in her family) and tells her life story, until she, too, is a 'giant' with a baby of her own. Encourage the children to pose questions of their own to investigate: for example, 'Do the tallest people have the biggest feet/heads/hands?' This activity illustrates the use of capital letters.

> **Vocabulary:** *big, bigger, short, shorter, small, smaller, tall, taller.*

 For **The same but different** (page 19) you could play a game spotlighting the differences and similarities between people. In a large space, such as a playground or hall, ask the class to move around while music is played. Stop the music and say (for example), 'Sit down if you have blond hair'; ask the remaining children how they are different from the ones sitting down. Continue the music, while the remaining children move around; continue, stopping the music and identifying a physical characteristic (blue/brown eyes, etc.), and asking the children who are still standing how they are different from the ones sitting down (they should identify all the features) until no child is left standing. You could include shoe sizes and features such as freckles, although sensitivity is needed if there are any children with disfigurements. This page gives the children an opportunity to complete simple sentences. A complementary activity for this sheet is available on the website (see Year 1 Activity 1).

> **Vocabulary:** *black, blond, blue, brown, curly, eyes, freckles, ginger, green, grey, hair, hazel, long, medium, short, straight, wavy.*

 **Match it: teachers' page** (page 20) could be linked with PE: ask the children to move along the ground in as many different ways as they can, and ask them which parts of their bodies they are using. Different groups could watch others moving, use the words for different types of movement and describe what they are doing. You could also talk about the body parts the animals use to help them to move: feet, fins, flippers, legs, paws, tail. This page gives the children a chance to extend their vocabulary. A complementary activity for this sheet is available on the website (see Year 1 Activity 2).

> **Vocabulary:** *fly, gallop, hop, jump, run, skip, slide, swim, walk, wriggle.*

 For **Is it living?** (page 21) the children could contribute to a display of living things: invite them to cut out pictures of living things from magazines or newspapers (you could also print some from Internet and CD-ROM sources), glue them on to the display and then write labels for them. The children could discuss with their groups beforehand to check that the things are, in fact, living. Ask them a series of questions to help them to decide if something is living: 'Does it need water?', 'Does it need air?', 'Will it die?' Discuss any dead animals or plants the children have seen. If children have had pets that have died this will need sensitive handling, but it can also give the children an opportunity to share their good memories of their pet. This page will help to extend the children's vocabulary. A complementary activity for this sheet is available on the website (see Year 1 Activity 3).

> **Vocabulary:** *air, alive, animal, breathe, drink, eat, feed, food, grow, living, move, plant, water.*

For **Staying alive** (page 22) you could set up a class 'pet shop' containing toy and model animals, books about animal care and equipment for caring for animals. Ask the children how they are going to look after The children should not touch their faces, especially their mouths and eyes, after touching animals. They should wash their hands after touching animals.

the 'animals' in the pet shop. Will they care for them all in exactly the same way, or do some of them need different care? Ask them what all the animals need. Also keep some animals such as snails in the classroom for a short time and discuss with the children how you are going to care for them: talk about their needs; food and drink. The animals also need air to breathe; you could show the children how to make sure that the animals can breathe. This activity will help to extend the children's vocabulary.

> **Vocabulary:** *air, breathe, drink, food, shelter, water.*

Growing plants

 On a **Plant search** (page 23) ask the children about the colours of the flowers of familiar plants, and if they are always that colour: for example, clover can be white or pink, but dandelions are always yellow. If no flowers can be seen on the plants it is important that the children know that they do have flowers, but at a different time of the year: encourage them to watch out for those plants flowering. Ask them if grass has flowers. They might not realise that grass is a flowering plant; the seeds of plants come from their flowers. If grass is kept short the flowers are constantly being cut off. Show the children different kinds of long grass and talk about the different flowers on them. Point out some of the dangers from plants: poisoning, scratching (from thorns) and stinging. This page gives the children the opportunity to write labels. A complementary activity for this sheet is available on the website (see Year 1 Activity 4).

> ⚠ Tell the children that they should not pull up wild plants and ask them if they know why.
>
> Before carrying out a 'plant search' you need to know about poisonous plants and any that are likely to be found that can irritate the skin. Warn the children not to touch them. Common plants to avoid touching include foxglove, laburnum, larkspur, lilac, lily of the valley, nettle, privet and wisteria pods and seeds.
>
> See also
> www.lamaze.com/baby/safety/articles/0,,159763_182630,00.html
>
> Ensure that the children wash their hands after touching plants.

> **Vocabulary:** *clover, dandelion, flower, grass, leaf, stem.*

For **Lisa's lunch** (page 24) the children could show the group the contents of their lunch boxes and talk about the foods they know come from plants. Ask if the other children can see any they have missed out. This sheet gives the children practice in writing labels. Always check if any of the children suffers from a food allergy before offering them foods to taste.

> **Vocabulary:** *apple, food, orange, plant, potato.*

 Tom's tomato (page 25) helps children to realise that the seeds bought in packets come from plants. They could look at the seeds of various plants, including apple, bean, beech, cucumber, horse chestnut, melon, oak, orange, pea, sunflower and tomato. Show them how to plant seeds taken from the plants. A cucumber can be cut so that the children have a slice each, containing seeds (which could be planted). Tomato, apple and sunflower seeds also germinate quickly in a warm place during the spring or summer (a polythene bag tied over the pot helps). This page offers the children a context in which to read and use captions. A complementary activity for this sheet is available on the website (see Year 1 Activity 5).

> **Vocabulary:** *flower, green, pot, seed, shoot, soil, tomato.*

For **Watering plants** (page 26) show the children some wilting flowers, pot plants and a stick of celery all in need of water. Ask them what they can do to make the plants better. Also show them some plants and flowers that have  been left too long to revive and let them try giving them water. Introduce the word *wilt* and talk about what happens to plants when left for a short time or for a long time without water. Help the children to set up a fair test to compare seeds that are watered with those that are not: for example, discuss the medium in which the seeds are planted; point out that if some seeds are planted in potting compost and some in soil, they will not know what caused any differences they observe – the type of soil, or whether or not the plants were watered. Ask the children how they will remember which seeds are to be to watered and which are not. This activity offers the children a chance to use the language of non-fiction texts.

> **Vocabulary:** *flower, plant, seed, water, wilt.*

For **Do plants need light?** (page 27) help the children to set up a fair test to compare seeds that are given light with those that are not: for example, discuss the medium in which the seeds are planted; point out that if some seeds are planted in potting compost and some in soil, they will not know what caused any differences they observe – the type of soil, or whether or not the plants were given light. Similarly, if some are watered and some are not, they will know if that is what is affecting them. Discuss how often the children should observe the seeds; for example, every day, every two days or every three days. The children might expect the seeds without light to die, but they usually grow much faster than those given light – however, they soon become straggly and unhealthy and pale, and they die. The children could record their observations of the seedlings on a wall chart. Afterwards, discuss the children's observations and ask them what they have learned. You could ask them about all the other things a seed needs in order to grow and the things that might stop it growing. *The Tiny Seed* by Eric Carle (Puffin) is useful. On this page the children write labels and complete simple sentences.

> **Vocabulary:** *dark, light, pale, plant, pot, seed, seedling, soil, sun, unhealthy.*

Roots (page 28) introduces children to the part of the plant they cannot usually see. After the children have examined plant roots, ask them what roots are for and what would happen if the roots were cut off. You could cut off the roots of a seedling or unwanted pot plant to find out. Talk about what happens when a plant is watered. Where does the water go and how does it get into the plant? Establish that plants take in water through their roots; roots also anchor them to the ground. This activity focuses on writing labels.

> **Vocabulary:** *anchor, leaf, roots, seedling, soil, stem.*

After the children have completed **Flower detective** (page 29), invite them to read out their answers. Discuss any differences. They could write about some tests they can think of for checking whether a flower or plant is real. Ask them what would happen if an artificial and a real plant or flower were put in a cupboard. Would it be the same at the end of the week? Help them to find

out; they should draw the plants and flowers before and after they are left in the cupboard and compare the real with the artificial ones. Point out that only living things can die. You could use this page to assess what the children have learned about living and non-living things and about what plants need in order to grow. This sheet requires the children to use phonological, contextual, grammatical and graphic knowledge.

> **Vocabulary:** *artificial, flower, light, living, real, soil, water.*

Sorting and using materials

For **The toy box** (page 30) you could create a display of toys labelled with words to describe the materials from which they are made, and a 'materials' word-bank. This page gives the children a chance to read and use captions.

> **Vocabulary:** *bendy, bouncy, dull, feel, floppy, hard, listen, look, material, rough, shiny, smooth, soft, stiff, stretchy.*

Guess what? (page 31) provides an opportunity to set up a 'treasure hunt' for the children: provide them each with a shoe box to fill using a list of materials (for example, 'something soft', 'something wet', 'something hard' and so on). The children will enjoy exploring slime: read *The Slimy Book* by Babette Cole (Collins Picture Lions) and then make a bowl of slime by mixing cornflour and water and colouring it green. Let the children explore the feel of the slime and talk about their observations. The children could suggest various items for each of the boxes on this page: the first could be anything made of metal or ceramics; the second could be imitation fur or fur fabric; the third could be brick or stone. This activity will help to extend the children's vocabulary.

> **Vocabulary:** *bendy, cold, dry, feel, floppy, hard, heavy, material, rough, slime, slimy, smooth, soft, stiff, warm, wet.*

On the bus (page 32) focuses on the properties of materials that produce sounds when the materials are moved. You could set up an exploration area in which the children can explore the sounds they can make from a collection of materials such as foil, metal, paper, plastic, stone and wood. They could tap them, rub them, crumple them. The children could also play a game in which one of them uses various objects to create sounds and the others have to listen and say what it is. This sheet asks the children to identify phonemes.

> **Vocabulary:** *bang, beep, click, clink, ding, scrape, scream, screech, shh, swish, tap, vroom, woof.*

Material search (page 33) introduces the names of common materials. Encourage the children to talk about the materials from which everyday objects are made. Ask them questions such as 'Could it be made of glass/paper?' and 'Why not?'; 'What would be good about that material?' or 'What would be bad about that material?' The children could also make observations of the materials used in and around their homes and share their observations in school. You could focus on the different materials from which the same things can be made (for example, chairs, tables, drainpipes, window frames, window panes and doors). You could also set up a labelled collection of

> ⚠ Do not let the children handle glass objects.

chairs made of different materials from around the school. The children could sort them by material (for example, plastic, wood, metal, fabric). This activity shows the children that information can be presented in different ways.

> **Vocabulary:** *glass, hard, material, metal, plastic, see-through, stone, strong, tough, transparent, wood.*

For **Wood** (page 34) you could set up an activity area in which the children can explore the properties of wood. At regular intervals, change the objects available. If possible, include a piece of ebony (for example,

 Point out the dangers of sharp tools and warn the children never to touch tools they come across. Teach them how to use safely those that are suitable.

from old piano keys) or lignum vitae (crown green bowls are made of this) and some wood shavings. Set different tasks: for example, 'Does all wood float?', 'How can we join pieces of wood?', 'Can you fold or crumple wood?' Invite a carpenter to show the children some of the things he or she does with wood: how to cut it, shape it and join it. This could be an opportunity to show the children how to use simple wood-working tools such as a hand-drill and a small saw. The children could also label wooden items in the classroom (chair, book box). This activity will help to extend the children's vocabulary.

> **Vocabulary:** *crumple, cut, float, fold, hard, heavy, join, light, material, shape, shave, strong, thick, thin, tough.*

For **Plastic** (page 35) you could set up an activity area in which the children can explore the properties of plastic. At regular intervals, change the objects available and set different tasks: for example, 'Does all plastic float?' and 'Can you fold plastic?' After the children have completed the activity, draw out the

properties of plastic: for example, it is waterproof, it comes in different colours, it can be *transparent* (introduce this word once the children have used terms they understand, such as 'see-through') and it can be made into different shapes. The children could also label plastic items in the classroom (ruler, beaker). This sheet will help the children to read and use captions.

> **Vocabulary:** *float, fold, hard, heavy, light, material, see-through, shape, thick, thin, transparent, waterproof.*

Before the children complete **Glass** (page 36), provide information books about glass. If possible, take the children to a glass works or

 Do not let the children handle glass objects.

glass-blower's workshop and help them to find out about the properties of glass and how it can be shaped. Discuss how this is different from materials such as wood and paper. Discuss why picture frames have glass in them and which other materials can be used instead, why windows are made of glass. The children could also look at the different kinds of glass used in windows, such as frosted glass and wired glass. The children could also label glass items in the classroom (window, mirror). This activity will help to extend the children's vocabulary.

> **Vocabulary:** *break, hard, heavy, light, material, melt, see-through, shape, sharp, smash, thick, thin, transparent, waterproof.*

For **Metal** (page 37) you could set up an activity area in which the children can explore the properties of metals. Include containers, large nails, scissors, spoons, forks, saucepans and foil. At regular intervals, change the objects available and set different tasks: for example, 'Does metal float?' and 'Can you fold metal?' After the children have completed the activity, draw out the properties of metal: for example, it is hard, it can be joined, it can be made into different shapes. Discuss why metal is a good material for making certain things. Also let the children compare objects that can be made of other materials: for example, buckets, shovels and cutlery. They could compare the weight and how easily they break. The children could also label metal items in the classroom (door handle, pencil sharpener). The children complete simple sentences in this activity.

> **Vocabulary:** *bendy, break, burn, fold, hard, heavy, light, material, melt, shape, sharp, strong, thick, thin, waterproof.*

All kinds of paper (page 38) encourages the children to notice the different kinds of paper used in the classroom; also talk about different papers they use at home. Discuss what makes each one

 Avoid ready-pasted wallpaper; the paste usually contains fungicides.

suitable for its purpose. You could set up an activity area in which the children can explore the properties of paper. Include containers, writing paper, paper towels, kitchen roll, toilet roll, gift wrapping, wallpaper, carbon paper, cardboard boxes, paper bags. At regular intervals, change the objects available and set different tasks: for example, 'What happens when paper gets wet?', 'Can you fold all kinds of paper?' and 'How can you join pieces of paper?' After the children have completed the activity, draw out the properties of paper: for example, it comes in different colours; pencils, pens and paint can be used to make marks on it; it can be made into boxes and bags. Discuss why paper is a good material for these things. This activity requires the children to read and follow simple instructions.

> **Vocabulary:** *bendy, break, brown, burn, colour, fold, glue, heavy, light, material, shape, stiff, strong, thick, thin, white.*

Let's make a window: 1 and **2** (pages 39–40) encourages the children to talk about their observations of real windows: the materials used for different windows and

 Provide only very small pieces of plastic and cling film. Warn the children of the dangers of suffocation; they should not put any plastic materials on their faces.

why they think these materials were chosen. Once the children have sorted the materials into sets ('good for windows' and 'not good for windows'), ask them what makes each material suitable or unsuitable for a window. Use the terms *see-through* and *transparent*. Discuss the ways in which the windows can be cut and joined to the model house. These pages require the children to read and follow instructions and to write simple sentences.

> **Vocabulary:** *cardboard, cling film, cloth, foil, glass, paper, see-through, stone, tissue, transparent, window.*

Before tackling **Magnetic fish** (page 41) the children should explore a collection of materials and magnets and talk about their observations. They could use horseshoe magnets, bar magnets, fridge magnets and magnetic letters. Introduce the term *attracted* for 'picked up' and ask the children to sort the materials they test into two sets ('attracted' and 'not attracted'). After they have explained how they are going to change the paper fish to make it magnetic, ask them to test their ideas. They could record what happened. Afterwards, the children could use magnets to play a magnetic fishing game with paper cut-out fish with staples or paper clips attached to them. This sheet requires the children to read and follow simple instructions and to write simple sentences.

> **Vocabulary:** *attract, magnet, metal, paper clip, staple.*

In **Towel test** (page 42) encourage the children to make their test of the papers fair. You could do this by demonstrating extremes: soak your hands before testing one paper and then put a tiny drop of water on one hand for testing another; ask if this is fair. Similarly, use a tiny piece of one paper and an enormous piece of another and ask if it is fair. This activity shows the children that information can be presented in different ways.

> **Vocabulary:** *dry, paper, soak, towel, wet.*

For **Teddy's rain hat** (page 43) begin by examining and discussing the materials from which the children's own waterproof clothes are made. Make some hats from different materials as shown below. When the children suggest ways of testing the hats, encourage them to make their test fair. You could do this by demonstrating extremes: test one hat by pouring an enormous amount of water over it, test another with only a drop; ask if this is fair. Similarly, make a tiny hat from one material and an enormous one from another and ask if it is fair. The hats could be tested by pouring a cupful of water from a watering can over the hat on the teddy bear's head. You could make the hats like this:

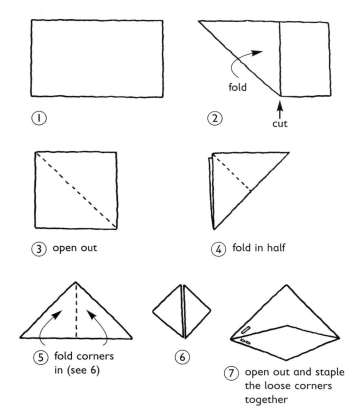

This activity illustrates that information can be presented in different ways.

> **Vocabulary:** *dry, paper, soak, water, waterproof, wet.*

Light and dark

For **A dark place** (page 44) give the children the opportunity to experience complete darkness. You could use a room with blackout curtains or a large, safe walk-in cupboard (the children could go into it in pairs with adult supervision, unless they are afraid of the dark or confined spaces). Ask them how they could tell what was in the cupboard and where the door was when it was closed. This sheet requires the children to write simple instructions, using the language of non-fiction texts.

> **Vocabulary:** *dark, feel, light, listen, smell, touch.*

After answering the questions on **Where does light come from?** (page 45), the children could test some of the objects by looking at them in a dark place (see page 44 notes). In this activity, the children have the chance to read and use captions.

Warn the children never to look at the Sun.

> **Vocabulary:** *light, shine.*

Before completing **Festivals of light** (page 46) the children could look at light sources such as torches in a bright place and then in a darkened place. Ask them what they notice. Encourage the children to make the lights they draw look light and to make the scene around the lights look like night. This sheet requires the children to write labels and to use labelled diagrams.

> **Vocabulary:** *bonfire, candle, Christmas, dark, diva, Divali, Hanukkah, hanukiah, light, night.*

For **Sight and light** (page 47) the children could make their own 'spy-boxes' with several small holes instead of one large one in the lid. They could find out how many holes need to be uncovered in order to see the colour of something inside the box. Is it the same for all colours? On this sheet the children read and follow simple instructions and write simple sentences.

> **Vocabulary:** *light, see, sight.*

Is it sunny? (page 48) gives the children an opportunity for an outdoor activity. They could compare their shadows on days when the sky is clear and when there is thin cloud cover. What do they think happens to the light from the Sun when the sky is cloudy? Does sunlight get through the clouds? How can they tell? You could also focus on the direction of shadows: the children should notice that all shadows face in the same direction at the same time, but that this changes during the day. In this activity, the children have the opportunity to produce extended captions.

> **Vocabulary:** *bright, cloud, hazy, light, shadow, sky, Sun.*

For **Reflectors** (page 49) ask the children to bring in reflective material: for example, clothes with reflective strips that they wear when walking home from school. To test how well they reflect light they could shine a torch on them in a dark place. They could also suggest materials which might make good reflectors and test them: fluorescent paper, tinsel. This page gives the children a chance to assemble information to write a simple non-chronological report.

> **Vocabulary:** *bright, light, reflect, reflector, shine, shiny.*

Pushes and pulls

How do they move? (page 50) focuses on the ways in which things move, rather than on what makes them move. It could be linked with PE; ask the children to move backwards, forwards, backwards and forwards, sideways, from side to side, up and down. They could also draw or paint lines showing movement in these directions; they could label their drawings or paintings and display them. On this sheet the children write simple sentences.

> **Vocabulary:** *backwards, down, forwards, move, round, sideways, spin, turn, up.*

For **Which parts move?** (page 51) some children could compare the movements of different teddy bears and dolls with their own movements: for example, dolls/bears with fixed arms and heads, some whose heads turn in a full circle. This activity offers the children an opportunity to use a labelled diagram.

> **Vocabulary:** *ankle, backwards and forwards, elbow, hip, knee, neck, round and round, shoulder, side to side, turn, up and down, wrist.*

Pushes and pulls (page 52) offers a chance to set up an activity area featuring toys to push and pull. Ask them to label the toys with ready-made 'push' and 'pull' stickers to show how they can make them move. The children could try making other things move: a box of blocks, a bucket of sand or a bag of shoes. Talk about the different directions in which they move the things and ask them to demonstrate the direction in which they pushed or pulled. They could draw pictures of what they did and add direction arrows for their pushes or pulls. This page gives the children a chance to follow simple instructions.

> **Vocabulary:** *move, pull, push, start.*

To make the car move in **Go!** (page 53) the children could use blocks to raise the ramp it is resting on, lift one side of the Warn the children not to try to move heavy things. table, tie string to the car, pull it or push it. Talk about other things in the classroom that the children can move. Which things can they not move? Why not? This page requires the children to write instructions.

> **Vocabulary:** *lift, pull, push, raise.*

Children's ideas for stopping the car in **Stop!** (page 54) might include taking hold of it, putting a barrier such as a box in front of it, and putting sand, carpet or another rough material on the ground. This activity involves producing extended captions.

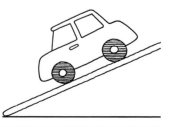

> **Vocabulary:** *block, crash, hold, rough, start, stop.*

Danger! (page 55) could be linked to work on road safety. You could show the children a road safety video, preferably one that shows that cars take a long time to stop when they are moving quickly. Also talk about safety at home and at school; point out the dangers of falling objects, especially heavy furniture like bookcases and tall piles of items, and the need to take care when opening and closing doors. This activity requires the children to produce extended captions.

> **Vocabulary:** *bump, fall, fast, harm, hurt, heavy, run over, sharp.*

Sound and hearing

Many of the activities in this section can be introduced using songs from *High Low Dolly Pepper* by Veronica Clark (A & C Black).

For **The sounds I hear** (page 56) invite the children to talk about the sounds they hear when they wake up and when they are in bed at night; they can include familiar sounds and any sounds they have heard but have not recognised right away. You could make a 'morning sounds' and 'night sounds' display: create two pictures of a house and the street outside it (one showing things that happen in the morning and one showing things that happen at night). The children could help to write labels for the sounds. You could record the sounds of a typical morning and ask the children to identify them and to say what time of the day they think it is. In this activity, the children create labelled diagrams and produce extended captions.

> **Vocabulary:** *hear, listen, noise, sound.*

For **A listening walk** (page 57) walk around the neighbourhood of the school and ask the children to identify any warning sounds they hear. Which sounds help them to keep safe? Talk about listening as well as looking for traffic and for pelican crossing signals. Do they know what the different sounds mean? Also talk about the ways in which cyclists and drivers warn people to take care. It is also useful to discuss hearing impairment: what difference it makes to people if they cannot hear and what devices there are to help them to do the things everyone else does. This activity requires the children to read and use captions.

> **Vocabulary:** *listen, noise, sound, warn.*

For **Sound search** (page 58) make a collection of sound-makers that the children can use to explore sounds: include a cabasa, corrugated cardboard, maracas, rattles, ridged wood sandpaper, sealed yogurt pots containing peas, gravel or sand, shakers and a washboard. Each child could be provided with his or her own sound-maker to be blown: a kazoo, recorder or whistle. Talk  about the words for the sounds. You could also sing songs about the sounds heard in different situations: for example, *Old Macdonald had a Farm* (or *a Zoo*). See also *Bingo Lingo* by Helen MacGregor (A & C Black). The children read and use captions and write labels in this activity.

> **Vocabulary:** *rattle, ring, scrape, scratch, sound, whistle.*

For **Sound-makers** (page 59) you could invite a musical group to visit the school to play and to talk to the children about their instruments or you could show the children a video of an

> ⚠ The children should not share items that have to be blown to make a sound unless they have been thoroughly cleaned and disinfected.

orchestra or band playing (this could be from a different part of the world). Talk about the sounds they hear and the ways in which the instruments make the sounds. Another starting point could be music that focuses on the sounds made by different instruments: for example, *Peter and the Wolf* (Prokofiev) or *A Young Person's Guide to the Orchestra* (Benjamin Britten). The children might notice that some instruments can produce sounds in different ways: for example, the bells and the tambourine can be shaken or struck with the hand. This activity extends the children's vocabulary and requires them to read and use captions.

> **Vocabulary:** *bang, blow, bow, pluck, scrape, shake, strike, tap.*

 Sound bingo (page 60) could be introduced with the song *Make your sound like mine* in *Bobby Shaftoe, clap your hands* by Sue Nicholls (A & C Black), or *Let your feet go tap, tap tap* or *Slap the sillies out* in *High Low Dolly Pepper* by Veronica Clark (A & C Black). Before playing this game it is useful to make a large-sized word-bank of all the words to be used. Practise making all the sounds and ask the children to identify the words for them. You could also make 'sound bingo' cards using photographs of objects whose sounds you have recorded: for example, a car engine or horn, a train, a burglar alarm, a baby crying, a dog barking, a lawnmower, an electric drill, a piano, a violin, a guitar. Play a sound from the tape recording and ask the children to cover the appropriate picture if they have it. When making sounds with their voices, encourage the children to feel their lips or throats. They should notice the movement. Introduce the word *vibrate*. This page helps the children to extend their vocabulary and to read and use captions.

> **Vocabulary:** *clap, hum, scream, shout, sing, snap, stamp, talk, tap, vibrate, whisper, whistle.*

For **Quiet and loud** (page 61) ask the children about places where people are very quiet: for example, in a hospital, when visiting a church or mosque, in a library. They could practise being very quiet. They could also practise loud sounds in a suitable place, such as the playground. Ask them to think of

> ⚠ Warn the children that loud sounds can damage their hearing. You could show them pictures of people who wear ear protection during their work: for example, machinery operators.

words that people might need to shout: for example 'Watch out!', 'Danger!', 'Help!', 'Hello!', or to call a dog's name when it is far off.

They could sing a loud song: for instance, *Watch out!* in *High Low Dolly Pepper* by Veronica Clark (A & C Black). Ask the children what they do if they do not want to hear a loud noise, and why. Do they cover their ears or move away from whatever is making the sound? What difference does this make? What do they do if they want to hear a quiet sound? Do they go closer to it or put their ear near to it? What difference does this make? This sheet requires the children to read and follow simple instructions and to read and use captions. The activity will help to extend their vocabulary.

> **Vocabulary:** *beep, buzz, drip, flush, honk, loud, quiet, rattle, ring, slam, snip, swish.*

In **Muffle it** (page 62) discuss why the child listening to the sounds could hear better without earmuffs. What did the earmuffs do? Ask the children why some sounds can be heard through earmuffs while others cannot. Some of them might be able to use the results of the investigation to arrange the sounds in order from quietest to loudest. On this page, the children read and follow simple instructions and use captions. The activity will help to extend their vocabulary.

> **Vocabulary:** *earmuffs, loud, louder, loudest, quiet, quieter, quietest.*

Far-off sounds: 1 and **2** (pages 63–64) encourage the children to think about the effects of distance on sounds and to predict which sounds they will be able to hear from the greatest distances and then

to suggest ways of testing their predictions. Some children can discuss this with a partner and make notes and draw their ideas, while others will need more guidance. After they have made their predictions (page 63), help them to plan an investigation. They could go into the playground to do this; some of them could make the sounds from as far away as possible, while the others listen and try to identify them. Those making the sounds could move closer to the others; help them to record which sounds could be heard from a long distance, which ones could be heard from a shorter distance and which ones could be heard only from close up. Ask the children to explain these results; discuss which sounds were the loudest. You could make a wall display depicting the playground and marking the distances at which the sounds could be heard. On these pages, the children read and follow simple instructions.

> **Vocabulary:** *close, faint, far, loud, near, quiet.*

Body jigsaw

Recognise that human bodies have similar parts

Which bits of the body jigsaw are missing?
- ## Write the words in the speech bubbles.

Word-bank

ankle	elbow	forehead	hip
knee	neck	toe	wrist

Teachers' note Introduce the activity with songs such as *One finger, one thumb keep moving*, adding different body parts as the song progresses. Use names for parts of the body that the children might not know, such as *ankle*, *forehead*, *shoulder* and *wrist*. As an extension activity, some children could make their own 'body jigsaw' by cutting out pictures of people from mail order catalogues.

Developing Science
Year 1
© **A & C BLACK**

Sense it

Understand that we have five senses

Which parts of their bodies are they using? ✔

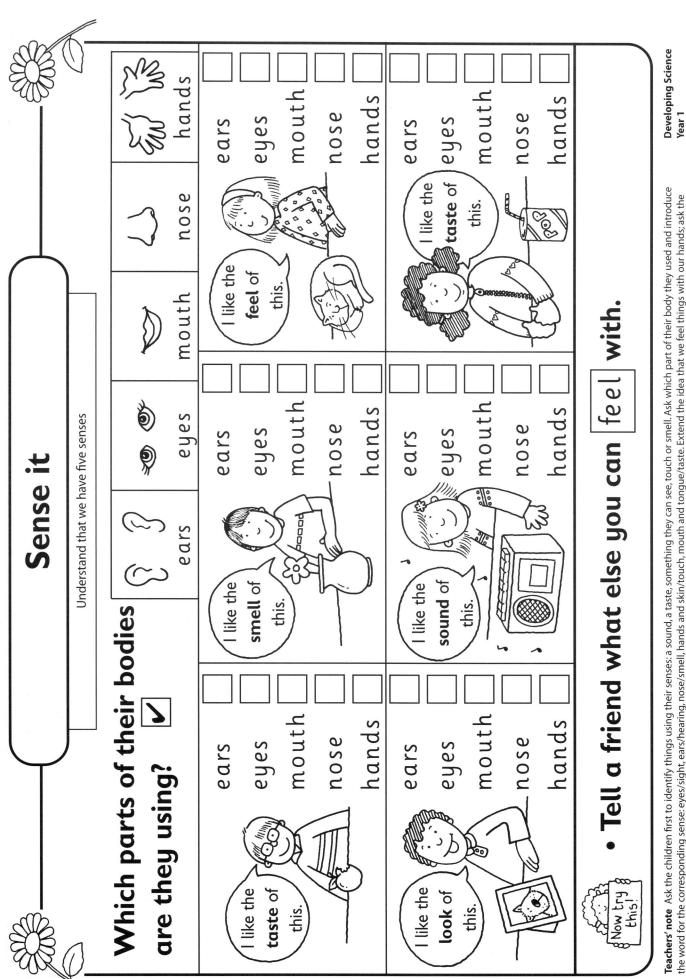

ears	eyes	mouth	nose	hands
☐	☐	☐	☐	☐

I like the **taste** of this.

- ears
- eyes
- mouth
- nose
- hands

I like the **smell** of this.

- ears
- eyes
- mouth
- nose
- hands

I like the **feel** of this.

- ears
- eyes
- mouth
- nose
- hands

I like the **look** of this.

- ears
- eyes
- mouth
- nose
- hands

I like the **sound** of this.

- ears
- eyes
- mouth
- nose
- hands

I like the **taste** of this.

- ears
- eyes
- mouth
- nose
- hands

Now try this!

- **Tell a friend what else you can** ☐ feel **with.**

Teachers' note Ask the children first to identify things using their senses: a sound, a taste, something they can see, touch or smell. Ask which part of their body they used and introduce the word for the corresponding sense: eyes/sight, ears/hearing, nose/smell, hands and skin/touch, mouth and tongue/taste. Extend the idea that we feel things with our hands; ask the children what other parts of the body they can feel things with, and lead them to the understanding that we feel things with our skin.

Developing Science
Year 1
© A & C BLACK

Is it an animal?

Understand that the term animal includes humans

Are these animals ? ✔ **or** ✘

grass ☐	spider ☐	goldfish ☐
crocodile ☐	girl ☐	cow ☐
daisy ☐	butterfly ☐	worm ☐
sheep ☐	boy ☐	duck ☐

Now try this!

What can animals do?

- **Write a sentence about what animals can do.**

Teachers' note Provide collections of pictures of animals (including humans and other mammals, reptiles, insects, birds and fish) and plants. Ask the children to sort the pictures into two sets: 'animal' and 'not animal'. Ask them how they can tell if something is an animal; draw attention to what animals can do: breathe, eat, drink, move around.

**Developing Science
Year 1**
© **A & C BLACK**

A growing family

Recognise that humans change as they grow older

Here is the Lee family.
Can you work out who they are?
• Write their names.

Anna (age 10)	Gran
Ben (age 15)	Grandad
Ella (age 1)	Mum
Paul (age 5)	Dad

Teachers' note The children should first make up families of toy people, dolls or pictures cut from magazines or brochures. Ask them how old the people in their pretend families are and how they can tell. After the activity, ask: 'How can you tell which is Gran?', 'How can you tell the difference between Gran and Mum?' As an extension activity, you could ask some children to make up another family from people cut out of magazines and to label them to show who are the mother and father, grandparents and so on.

Happy families: 1

Match young and adults of the same animals

caterpillar	butterfly	chick	hen
girl	woman	boy	man
lion cub	lion	tadpole	frog
foal	horse	calf	cow

Teachers' note Use this with page 17. The children should first look at live animals with their young (for example, on a visit to a farm, park, wildlife centre or pet shop, or in the school grounds), or at pictures and videos. Shuffle the cards cut out from the sheet and ask the children to match the young animals with the ones they will be like when they grow up. Ask the children to describe differences – in size, shape, parts of their bodies. Continued on page 17.

Developing Science Year 1
© A & C BLACK

Happy families: 2

Match young and adults of the same animals

lamb

sheep

piglet

pig

duckling

duck

tiger cub

tiger

kitten

cat

puppy

dog

kid

goat

owlet

owl

Teachers' note Continued from page 16. Talk about, and show pictures and videos of, the changes that happen in the life cycles of animals such as butterflies, dragonflies, frogs and toads. Introduce vocabulary connected with these changes (see page 5).

Developing Science
Year 1
© A & C BLACK

From shortest to tallest

Make suggestions about growing older

- ## Cut out each set of people.
- ## Put them in order: | shortest | ⟶ | tallest |

  ## Is the tallest the oldest?

I am 5.

Rosie

I am 18.

James

I am 14.

Anna

I am 20.

Jenny

I am 50.

Jack

I am 10.

Rashmi

Now try this!

Do the tallest people have the biggest feet?

- ## Tell a friend how to find out.

Teachers' note Invite the children to bring in group photographs of their families. Ask them how they can tell who is the oldest and who is the youngest. Will the older people be taller than the younger people? Encourage them to show the class their photographs, to talk about them and to answer questions such as 'Is x older than y?', 'Is x taller than y?', 'Who is the oldest person in the picture?', 'Is he/she the oldest?'

Developing Science
Year 1
© A & C BLACK

The same but different

Understand that there are differences between humans

- **Look at the faces.**
- **Colour the** differences .

How are they the same **?**

They both have _____ .
They both have _____ .
They both have _____ .
They both have _____ .

Word-bank

ears
neck
eyes
nose
hair
one
mouth
two

Now try this!

- **Draw your face.**
- **Draw a friend's face.**

How are they different **?**

Teachers' note Begin by asking two children to come to the front. Ask the others to say how they are the same and how they are different. Record their responses. The children could also look in a mirror and compare their face with that of a partner. Encourage them to name parts of the face and colours and shapes.

**Developing Science
Year 1**
© A & C BLACK

Match it: teachers' page ICT

Compare how animals move

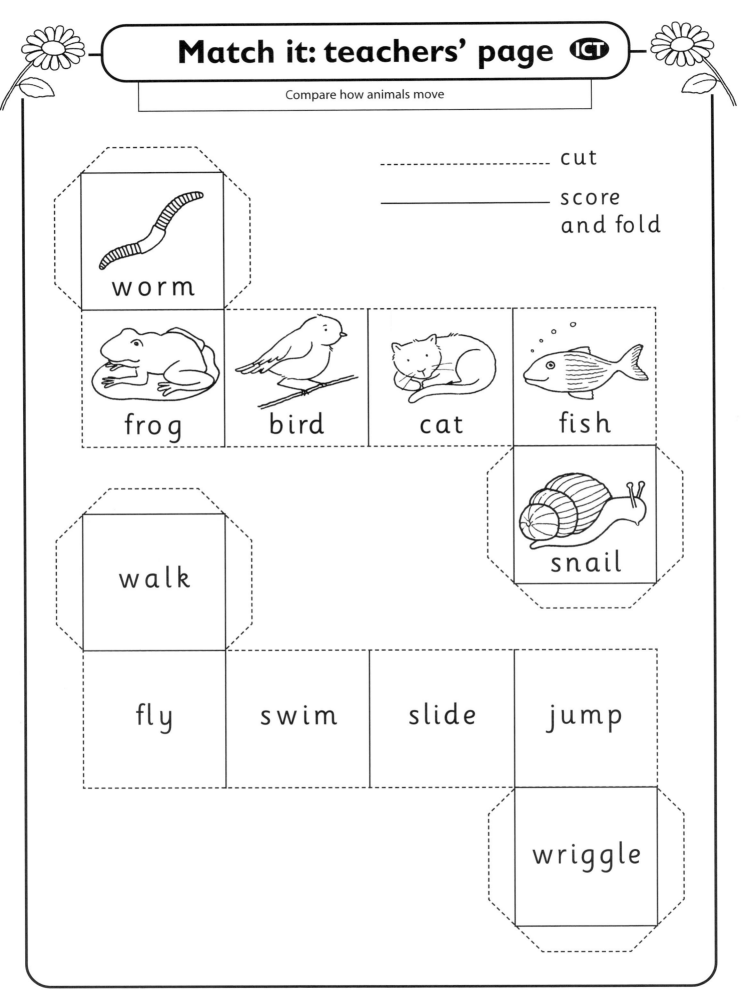

- - - - - - - - - - - - cut

——————— score
and fold

worm

frog   bird   cat   fish

snail

walk

fly   swim   slide   jump

wriggle

Teachers' note First allow children to observe animals moving: they could watch birds in the school grounds, talk about how their pets move, watch videos. Introduce words for movement (see page 6). Make up the dice to play a matching game. The children roll the animal die and read out the animal's name. Then they roll the movement die, read out and act the movement. Does the movement match the animal?

Developing Science
Year 1
© **A & C BLACK**

Is it living?

Understand that animals are living

- **Find** living **things in the picture.**
- **Colour the living things.**

Now try this!

- **Draw some living things in your school grounds.**
- **Write the words.**

Teachers' note Begin by taking the children for a walk round the school grounds to look for living things. List their responses and discuss them back in the classroom: ask them how they knew these things were living. Focus on movement and the need for food and water.

Developing Science
Year 1
© A & C BLACK

Staying alive

What do the animals need?

- **Draw lines of different colours.**

meat   dog   grass

water   bird   seeds

nuts   cow   shelter

What do you need?

Now try this!

- **Draw and label the things you need to stay alive.**

Teachers' note You could begin by talking about a pet, such as a gerbil, cat or dog, or animals kept in the classroom for a short time, such as snails. Ask the children how they would look after the animal. Focus on food and drink. Tell the children to use different coloured lines to match each animal to its various needs: for example, a blue line for matching any animal to water, etc.

Developing Science
Year 1
© **A & C BLACK**

Recognise that plants have leaves, stems and flowers

- **Colour the** plants .
- **Label the parts.**

flower

stem

leaf

clover

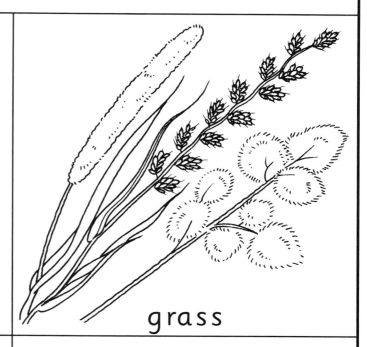

grass

dandelion

another plant I found

Now try this!

- **Draw and label three other plants.**

Teachers' note The children first need to look at wild plants growing around the school. Help them to identify a few common plants such as those shown on this page. Talk about the parts they can see that all green plants have: a stem (or stems), leaves and flowers. Ask them to point out these parts on the plants they see growing.

**Developing Science
Year 1**
© A & C BLACK

Lisa's lunch

Understand that plants provide food for humans

Which foods come from plants **?** ✔ **or** ✘

peas ☐

fish ☐

chips ☐

orange juice ☐

apple ☐

- **Draw your lunch.**
- **Label the foods from plants.**

Teachers' note Show the children some common and less common food plants and ask which they have eaten: for example, artichoke, cabbage, carrot, maize, mango, melon, pea, pear, potato, squash. Arrange a tasting session for those eaten raw. Help the children to recognise food plants they may have seen only in processed form: show them containers alongside the raw plants – beetroot (a jar of beets), maize (tinned sweetcorn), potato (chips/crisps), wheat (flour/bread).

Developing Science
Year 1
© **A & C BLACK**

Tom's tomato

Understand that plants grow from seeds

• **Put the pictures in order.**

 • **Match the words to the pictures.**

Tomatoes grew from the flowers.	Tom planted a seed from a tomato.
A green shoot grew.	Leaves and flowers grew on the shoot.

Teachers' note Show the children some packets of seeds; let them examine the seeds and look at the pictures on the packets. Ask them what kind of plant each seed will grow into. Also ask them if they know where the seeds come from. Cut open a tomato and let them see the seeds. What kind of plant do they think will grow from the seeds?

Developing Science
Year 1
© A & C BLACK

25

Watering plants

Conclude that plants need water to grow

What will happen to the plants?

- Draw and write in the chart.

	water	no water
seeds		
a plant		

What do these flowers need?

- Write a sentence.

Now try this!

Teachers' note Use this page to encourage the children to predict what will happen to seeds that they plant (those they water and those they do not water). They could also predict what will happen to pot plants that are not watered. After drawing their predictions the children could suggest how they could test their predictions.

Developing Science
Year 1
© A & C BLACK

Do plants need light?

Conclude that plants need light to grow

- **Find out if plants need** light .
- **Draw and write what you will do.**

Word-bank
dark seed
light soil
pot sun

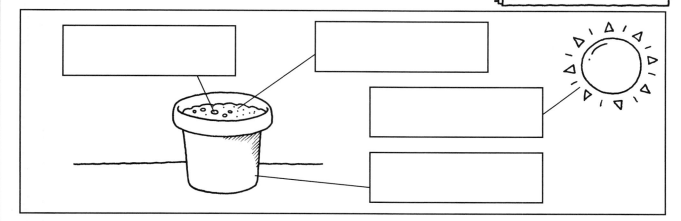

We will plant a seed in some _____.
We will put it in the _____.

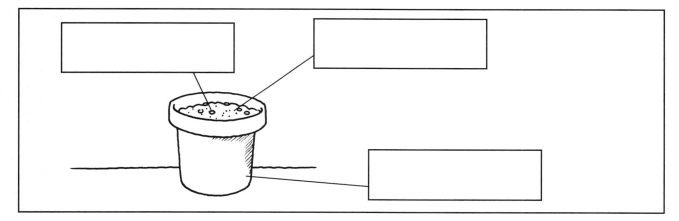

We will plant a seed in some _____.
We will put it in the _____.

Now try this!

- **Draw two pictures to show what happened.**
- **Write a sentence for each picture.**

Teachers' note Help the children to plan an investigation to find out if plants need light. Ask them what they can do, and talk about how it can be carried out in the classroom. Where can they put the seeds that are to have no light? Point out that the two sets of seeds will be treated in the same way except that one will be given light and one will not.

**Developing Science
Year 1**
© A & C BLACK

Roots

Understand that plants have roots

What is under the soil?

- **Finish the picture.**
- **Write labels.**

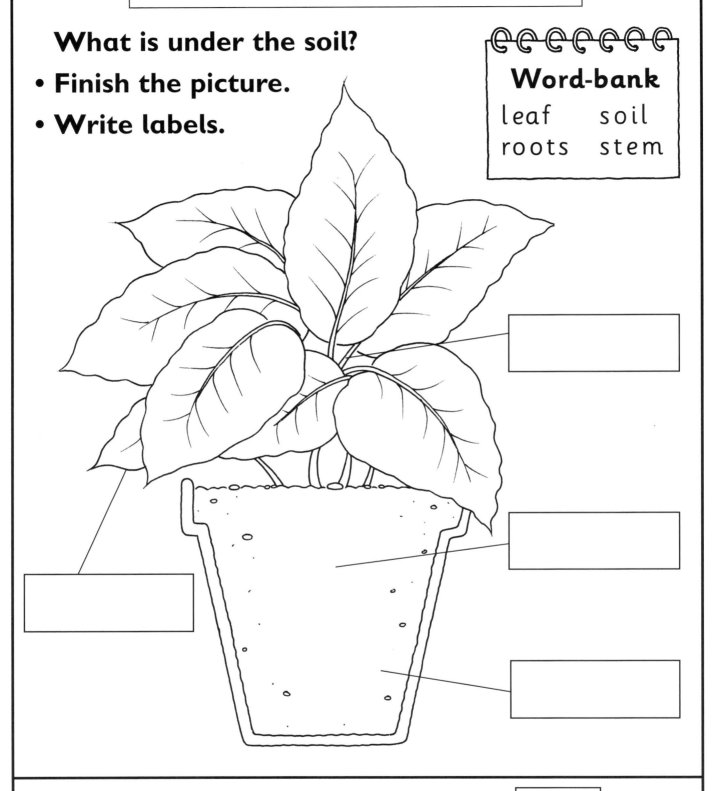

 • **Draw and write about the** roots **of another plant.**

Teachers' note The children first need to look at the roots of seedlings they have grown (see also page 27) and the roots of pot plants. Ask them about the shape and colour of the roots, and if all roots are the same. They should notice that roots are white, and that the bigger the plant the bigger the roots.

Developing Science
Year 1
© A & C BLACK

Flower detective

Recognise that real plants are living but artificial ones are not

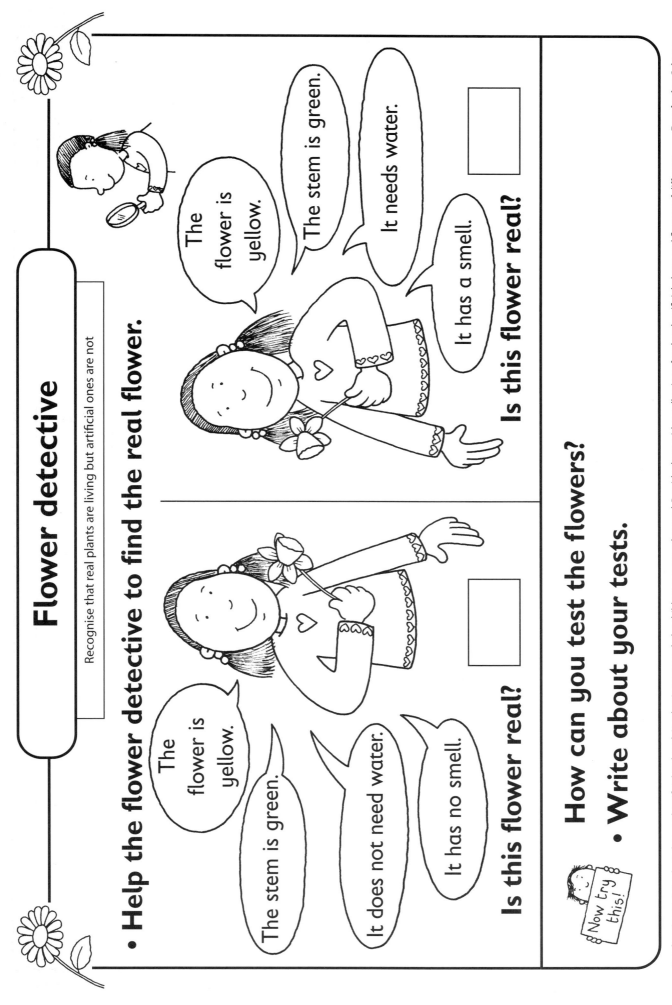

- **Help the flower detective to find the real flower.**

The flower is yellow.

The stem is green.

It does not need water.

It has no smell.

Is this flower real?

The flower is yellow.

The stem is green.

It needs water.

It has a smell.

Is this flower real?

- **How can you test the flowers?**
- **Write about your tests.**

Now try this!

Teachers' note Introduce the word *artificial* and explain what it means; ask the children to repeat the word. Provide them with a collection of real and artificial plants and flowers of different kinds and materials, including plastic, silk, etc. to sort into two sets ('real' and 'artificial'). They should first look at them from a distance and then look at them close up and handle them. How can they tell which is which?

Developing Science
Year 1
© A & C BLACK

The toy box

Understand that materials have many properties

- **Look at the toys.**
- **Join the words to the pictures.**

| floppy | shiny | hard |

| stretchy | | soft |

| | | dull |

| bouncy |

- **Next to the toy box draw:**
  - **something** rough
  - **something** smooth .

Teachers' note The children first need to handle various objects made from different materials, to talk about their observations and to use words for describing materials (see page 7). Read the words in the boxes together and ask the children to find things in the classroom (or in a collection of objects) that the words describe.

Developing Science
Year 1
© **A & C BLACK**

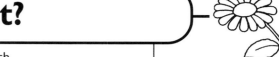

Guess what?

What could be in the box?

 It feels hard.

It feels smooth.

It feels cold.

 It feels stiff.

 It feels soft.

It feels smooth.

It feels floppy.

 It feels warm.

 It feels rough.

It feels hard.

It feels heavy.

 It feels stiff.

 Now try this!

- **Put something in a box.**
- **Tell a friend what it feels like.**
- **Ask your friend to guess what it is.**

Teachers' note You could introduce the activity by providing a 'feely box' containing objects that the children have to identify by touch alone. As they handle the objects, encourage them to talk about what they feel like. Children who need more support could start by guessing an item that fulfilled just one or two of the criteria mentioned, while others could be encouraged to think of more words to add to the description once they had guessed an object that fitted all four criteria.

Developing Science
Year 1
© **A & C BLACK**

On the bus

• **Match the things to the** sounds.

the wipers on the bus

swish, swish, swish

vroom, vroom, vroom

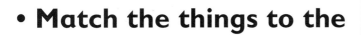

the people on the bus

shh, shh, shh

the money on the bus

clink, clink, clink

the dogs on the bus

woof, woof, woof

the babies on the bus

waah, waah, waah

the engine on the bus

the bell on the bus

ding, ding, ding

Now try this!

• **Draw and write about other sounds on a bus.**

Teachers' note Begin by singing *The Wheels on the Bus* with the children and inviting them to make up their own verses about sounds they might hear on a bus. Encourage them to use words that describe sounds, including onomatopoeic words such as 'ding, ding' and 'vroom, vroom'. In the extension activity they could write the words for the sound of tyres (screech), a horn (beep, beep) and so on.

Developing Science
Year 1
© A & C BLACK

Material search

Recognise that everyday objects can be made from the same materials

- **Look around your school.**

  What are things made of?

	glass	plastic	metal	wood	stone
steps					
door					
window					
pipe					

- **Look at other things.**

  What are they made of?
- **Make another chart.**

Teachers' note Take the children for a walk round the school and draw their attention to the materials from which parts of the building and its surroundings are made. Ask them why a particular material is good: for example, because it is strong, hard, you can see through it or it lets light through. Have they seen the same type of things made of other materials? For example, window frames can be made of wood, plastic or metal; drainpipes can be made of plastic or metal.

Developing Science
Year 1
© A & C BLACK

Wood

Understand that materials can be sorted in a variety of ways

Can these be made of wood ? or

chair ☐

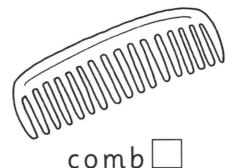

comb ☐

pan ☐

mug ☐

bowl ☐

wheel ☐

T-shirt ☐

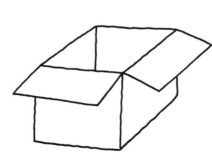

box ☐

bottle ☐

Now try this!

- **Draw three other things that can be made of wood.**

Can you think of three things that cannot be made of wood? Draw them.

Teachers' note Provide a collection of objects and ask the children to sort them by material. Ask them which things are made of wood, and if they could be made of anything else. After they have completed the activity sheet, ask them to explain their answers: for example, why a bottle, a pan or a T-shirt cannot be made of wood.

Developing Science
Year 1
© A & C BLACK

Plastic

Understand that materials can be used in a variety of ways

- **Cut out the pictures.**   - **Sort them.**

| can be plastic | cannot be plastic |

pan

mug

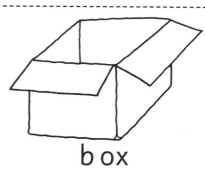

box

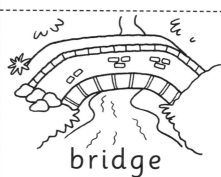

ball

shorts

bridge

house

spoon

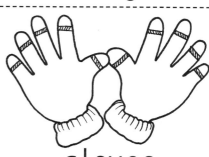

gloves

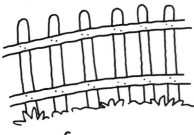

fence

key

bag

Teachers' note Provide a collection of objects and ask the children to sort them by material. Ask them which things are made of plastic, and if they could be made of anything else. Provide a sheet of paper onto which the children can glue the pictures in two sets: 'can be plastic' and 'cannot be plastic'. After they have completed the activity sheet, ask them to explain their answers: for example, why a pan or a bridge cannot be made of plastic.

Developing Science
Year 1
© A & C BLACK

Glass

Understand that materials can be used in a variety of ways

- **Circle the things that are made of $\boxed{\text{glass}}$.**

Now try this!

- **Draw something else made of glass. Why is glass a good material for it to be made of?**

Teachers' note Begin by asking the children what they know about glass and why they are not allowed to handle it in school. Which glass objects do they have to treat with special care at home? When they have completed the activity, ask why glass is good for the uses in the picture and which other materials can be used instead.

Developing Science
Year 1
© **A & C BLACK**

Metal

Use appropriate vocabulary to describe materials

Why is metal **good for these?**

Word-bank
burn
break
hard
sharp
strong

pan

It does not _____.

hammer

It is _____.

car

It is _____.

knife

It can be _____.

bucket

It does not _____.

Now try this!

- **Draw two other metal things.**

Why is metal a good material for them to be made of?

Teachers' note Provide a collection of metal objects and ask the children in what ways they are similar and different: include a drinks can, a hammer, a toy car, saucepans (heavy and light), a kettle. The children should handle the objects as well as look at them. Ask questions such as 'Is metal always heavy?' Establish that some metal things are very light (drinks cans) and others are heavy (hammer).

Developing Science
Year 1
© **A & C BLACK**

All kinds of paper

You need

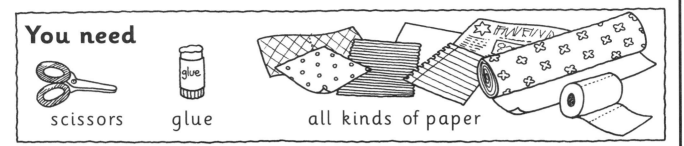

scissors   glue   all kinds of paper

- **Cut out pieces of** boxed{paper} **.**
- **Glue them onto the pictures.**

a present

a notebook

a toilet roll

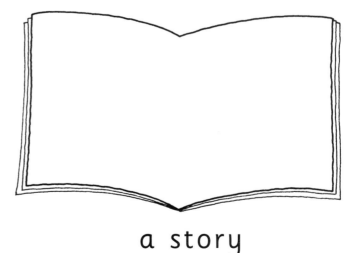

a story

Now try this!

- **Draw another paper thing.**
- **Glue the right kind of paper onto your picture.**

Teachers' note Give the children a collection of papers and cardboards and ask them to find different ways of grouping them: for example, rough/smooth, dull/shiny, thick/thin, bendy/stiff. Read the instructions on this page with them and talk about the properties of the different papers; ask them to choose the best kind of paper for each purpose.

Developing Science Year 1
© **A & C BLACK**

Let's make a window: 1

Understand that materials can be used in a variety of ways

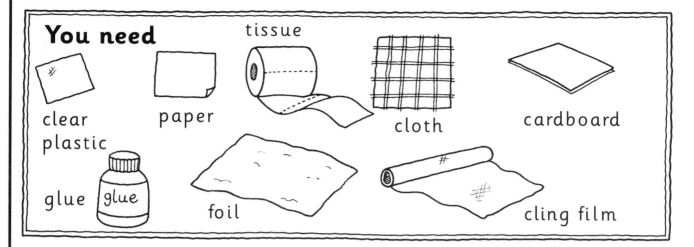

You need

clear plastic

paper

tissue

cloth

cardboard

glue

foil

cling film

You are going to make a window for a model house.

 Never put cling film or polythene on your face.

• Sort the materials.

Good for windows

Not good for windows

Teachers' note Use this with page 40. The children should first make a simple model house from a box. Ask them to think about the best materials for a window. Why can they not use glass? Discuss its good qualities for real windows and the dangers of using it in school; mention also the difficulty in cutting it. What other materials can they use? Ask them what they need to look for in a material for a window. Continued on page 40.

Developing Science
Year 1
© A & C BLACK

Let's make a window: 2

Use appropriate vocabulary to describe materials

You are going to make a
window for a model house.

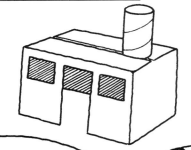

• **Fill in the gaps.**

Shall we
use cloth?

No. _____

_____

Shall we
use paper?

No. _____

_____

Shall we
use stone?

No. _____

_____

Shall we
use glass?

No. _____

_____

Now try
this!

What would you use? Write why it is good for making a window.

Teachers' note Continued from page 39. You could begin by asking the children similar questions to those on this page and holding up the relevant materials. Model the answers and then encourage the children to give their own reasons why they would not use each material.

**Developing Science
Year 1**
© A & C BLACK

Magnetic fish

Recognise that some materials are magnetic

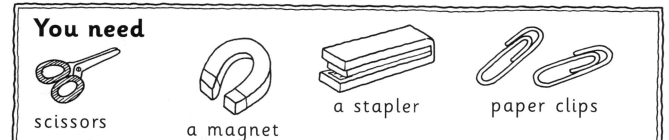

You need

scissors   a magnet   a stapler   paper clips

- **Cut out the fish.**

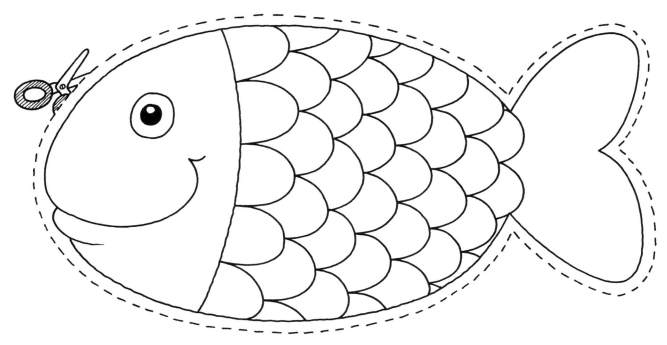

Does a magnet **pick up the fish?** _____

What can you do?

Teachers' note Ask the children to predict whether a magnet will pick up the paper fish and to say why or why not. Invite them to suggest ways of changing the fish so that the magnet will pick it up. What materials can they use and how can they fasten them to the fish? They can draw and write about their ideas on this page. As an extension activity, some children could make their own games using magnets, such as magnetic football or a magnetic racing car track.

Developing Science
Year 1
© A & C BLACK

Towel test

Test whether paper is suitable for a particular purpose

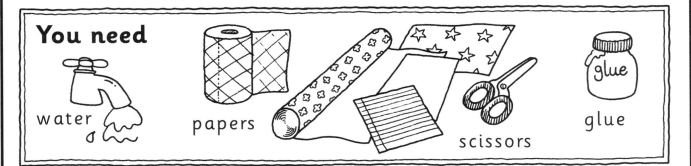

You need

water papers scissors glue

Which papers are good for drying hands?

- **Fill in the table.**

paper	☹	😐	☺
Stick the paper here			
Stick the paper here			
Stick the paper here			
Stick the paper here			

Now try this!

- **Draw a picture to show how you tested the papers.**
- **Write about the tests.**

Teachers' note The children could look at a collection of paper towels and compare them with other kinds of paper; ask them how they are similar/different. Ask them to suggest ways of testing a collection of papers to find out which is best for drying wet hands (see page 9). They should glue a piece of each paper they test onto the chart and tick the appropriate column to show how well it dried their hands.

Developing Science
Year 1
© A & C BLACK

Teddy's rain hat

Test whether materials are waterproof

You need

a teddy bear

a watering can

water

hats made from different materials

Which material will be best for a rain hat?

- **Fill in the table.**

material	☹	😐	😊

- **Write about how you tested the materials.**

Teachers' note Ask the children to suggest ways of testing a collection of materials made into hats to find out which is best for a rain hat (see page 9). They should glue a piece of each material they test onto the water chart and tick the appropriate column to show how well it kept teddy's head dry.

Developing Science
Year 1
© A & C BLACK

A dark place

Understand that light is essential for seeing things

Jake is going into a dark room.

There are no lights.

• **Tell him how to find out what is in there.**

• **Draw and write about waking up in the dark.**

Now try this!

Teachers' note Talk about the children's experiences of darkness: for example, waking up during the night. Ask them how they found their way around or found objects in the dark. Which senses did they use? Encourage them to use these experiences to help them to write instructions for finding things in a dark place.

**Developing Science
Year 1**
© A & C BLACK

44

Where does light come from?

Recognise that there are many sources of light

Does light come from these things? ✔ or ✖

leaf ☐

television ☐

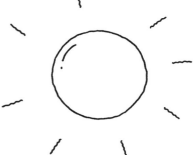

sun ☐

fire ☐

mirror ☐

torch ☐

mug ☐

cooker ☐

tap ☐

Now try this!

• **Draw three other things that have lights.**

Teachers' note Take the children for a walk round the school to look for sources of light (for example, computer monitors, warning lights, on/off lights, ceiling and wall lights, light coming from heat sources, lights on equipment). Also discuss the source of the light coming through windows (the Sun).

**Developing Science
Year 1**
© A & C BLACK

Festivals of light

- **Draw the** lights.
- **Write the captions.**

Word-bank

Bonfire night   Divali
Christmas   Hanukkah

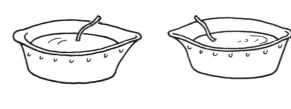

Now try this!

Are the lights lit at night or in the daytime?

Why?

Write a sentence.

Teachers' note Link this to work in religious education. Talk about the children's experiences of festivals and celebrations featuring light. Ask them when the lights are lit and why they are lit at night.

Developing Science
Year 1
© A & C BLACK

46

Sight and light

Understand that objects cannot be seen in darkness

You need a shoe box like this:

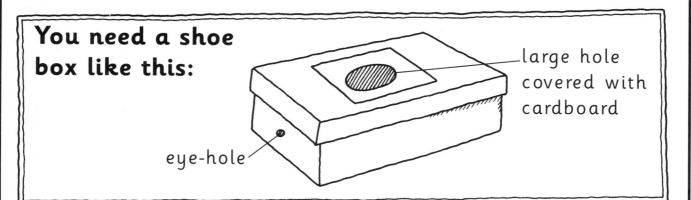

large hole covered with cardboard

eye-hole

- **Work with a partner.**
- **Put something in the box.**
- **Ask your partner to look through the eye-hole.**

Don't let your partner see.

The lid has to stay on.

Can they see what is inside? _____

What can they do to see it? _____

_____

_____

Now try this!

- **Complete the sentence:**

We can see things only if there is _____.

Teachers' note Prepare a shoe box as shown in the picture. Put something in the box and ask the children how they can find out what is in the box without opening it or touching it in any way. Let them look through the eye-hole. Can they see what is inside? Why not? Ask them what they can do (apart from taking off the lid or shaking the box) so that they can see what is inside it.

Developing Science
Year 1
© A & C BLACK

Is it sunny?

Recognise that the Sun is the source of light for the Earth

Is it ⬚sunny⬚ in these pictures?

- Cross out the wrong words.

How can you tell if it is sunny?

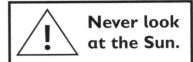

Never look at the Sun.

It is / is not sunny.

I can tell because

_____

_____ .

It is / is not sunny.

I can tell because

_____

_____ .

Now try this!

- **Draw your playground on a sunny day.**

Teachers' note On a day when it is sunny with some clouds (but not while the Sun is directly overhead), take the children outside. Ask them to turn their backs to the Sun. Can they tell when the Sun goes behind a cloud? How? Draw their attention to their shadows.

Developing Science
Year 1
© A & C BLACK

Reflectors

Find out where a reflector will shine brightly

Which are good reflectors **?** ✔ **or** ✘

a cat's eyes ☐

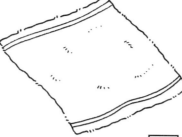

a towel ☐

a bike reflector ☐

reflectors on trainers ☐

a stone ☐

foil ☐

How can you test reflectors?

- **Write about your tests.**
- **Draw some other reflectors.**

_____

_____

_____

_____

Teachers' note Provide a collection of shiny things that are not light sources. The children could test them in a dark place to check that they are not sources of light before investigating whether or not they reflect light. You could challenge some children to make 'road safety' reflectors for a teddy bear (or to fix onto an old jacket to help to keep someone safe when they are out walking in the evening).

Developing Science
Year 1
© A & C BLACK

How do they move?

Understand that there are many sorts of movement

• **Look at the picture.**
How do the things | move | **?**

Word-bank
backwards
forwards
round and round
up and down

• **Write on the chart.**

	How it moves
swing	
seesaw	
roundabout	
bike	
gate	
skipping rope	

Now try this!

• **Find something at school that moves from side to side.**

Teachers' note Begin by taking the children for a walk round the school; ask them to point out anything they see moving. Help them to use vocabulary to describe the movements: *backwards, backwards and forwards, forwards, round and round, side to side, up and down.*

Developing Science
Year 1
© A & C BLACK

50

Which parts move?

Describe different ways of moving

- **Look at a teddy bear.**
- **Move its head, arms and legs.**
  Do they | move | **like yours?** ✔ **or** ✘

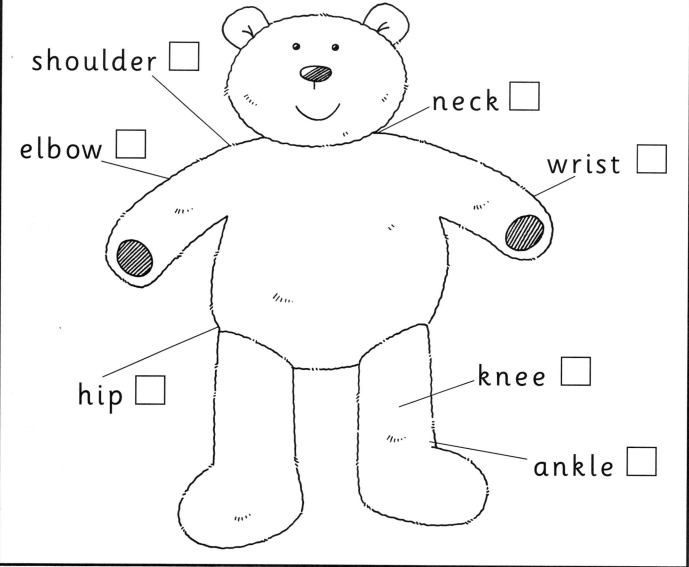

shoulder ☐

neck ☐

elbow ☐

wrist ☐

hip ☐

knee ☐

ankle ☐

Now try this!

- **See how another teddy or doll moves.**
- **Draw the parts that move like yours.**
- **Write the words.**

Teachers' note This could be linked with work on **Ourselves** (pages 12–22). Remind the children of the names of the parts of their bodies that move, especially the joints: *ankle, elbow, hip, knee, neck, shoulder, wrist*. Provide a teddy bear with some moving parts, and invite the children to move parts of it and then the same parts of themselves. Ask if the teddy bear moves in the same way. Ask them to describe how its movements differ from theirs.

Developing Science
Year 1
© **A & C BLACK**

Pushes and pulls

Identify similarities and differences between movements

- **Circle the pushes and pulls:**

pushes in (blue)   pulls in (red)

Now try this!

- **Draw and label things at home:**
  - **things you** push
  - **things you** pull .

Teachers' note You could begin by helping the children to identify things they push and pull in the classroom: drawers, doors, trolleys, boxes. Demonstrate the movements and invite the children to call out 'push' or 'pull' as appropriate. They could label each side of the classroom door 'push' and 'pull'.

Developing Science
Year 1
© **A & C BLACK**

Go!

How can you make the car go?
• Write instructions.

Word-bank
lift   push
pull   slope

_____
_____
_____

_____
_____
_____

_____
_____
_____

_____
_____
_____

Now try this!

• Draw something else you can move.
How can you move it?

Teachers' note Encourage the children to talk about what they can see in the pictures. Show them a toy car in similar situations and ask them how they can make it move (ask them to describe rather than demonstrate). After they have completed the activity sheet let them try their ideas to see how well they work.

Developing Science
Year 1
© A & C BLACK

Stop!

Understand that pushing or pulling makes things stop moving

How can you stop the toy car moving?
- **Draw your ideas.**
- **Write the words.**

Think of different ways.

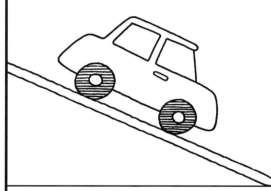

_____
_____
_____
_____

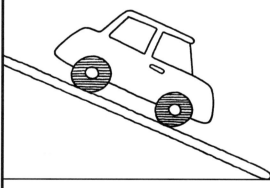

_____
_____
_____
_____

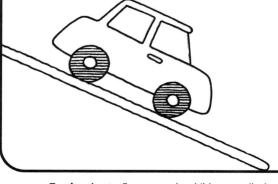

_____
_____
_____
_____

Teachers' note Encourage the children to talk about what they can see in the pictures. Show them a toy car in similar situations and ask them how they can stop it moving (ask them to describe rather than demonstrate). After they have completed the activity sheet, let the children try their ideas to see how well they work.

Developing Science
Year 1
© A & C BLACK

54

Danger!

How can moving things hurt you?

- **Write about the danger from moving objects.**

- **Draw a moving toy that could hurt you.**

Teachers' note Ask the children if they have ever been hurt by something that moves: for example, a ball, another child running, a swing, seesaw or bike. Ask them why it hurt, and talk about the dangers that come from fast-moving, heavy or sharp things.

**Developing Science
Year 1**
© A & C BLACK

The sounds I hear

Recognise that there are many different sources of sounds

- **Write and draw what you** hear **in the morning.**

- **Write and draw what you** hear **at night.**

Now try this!

- **Write about:**
  - **a sound that wakes you up**
  - **a sound that sends you to sleep.**

Teachers' note Ask the children to think about what it is like when they wake up in the morning. How do they know what is going on in and around their home? When they are in bed, what do they hear? Talk about the sounds they like and those they do not like.

Developing Science
Year 1
© A & C BLACK

A listening walk

Understand that hearing helps us recognise hazards

What did you hear ? ✔ or ✘

car ☐

bird ☐

lawnmower ☐

people ☐

fire engine ☐

ambulance ☐

police car ☐

horse ☐

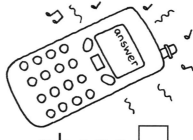

phone ☐

dog ☐

cat ☐

baby ☐

Now try this!

Which sound was the loudest ?
Which sound was the quietest ?

Teachers' note This page could be used to record the sounds heard during a 'listening walk'; or you could make a tape recording of sounds and ask the children if they can identify any of those shown in the pictures. Discuss which of the sounds they have heard could indicate danger: for example, a car horn.

**Developing Science
Year 1
© A & C BLACK**

Sound search

Recognise that we can describe sounds in many ways

- **Draw things that make these** sounds.
- **Write labels.**

ring 	rattle 
scratch 	whistle 

- **Find something that makes another kind of sound.**
- **Write the sound it makes.**

Teachers' note You could begin by making different sounds and asking the children if they know the words for them: for example (in addition to those on this page), bang, buzz, ping, scrape, squeak, tap, whistle. Provide a collection of objects with which the children can make sounds (see page 10).

Developing Science
Year 1
© **A & C BLACK**

Sound-makers

Understand that there are many different ways to make sounds

How do they make a sound ?

• **Sort the instruments into sets.**

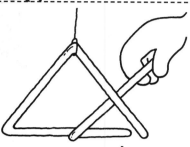 triangle	 tambourine	 drum
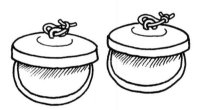 castanets	 recorder	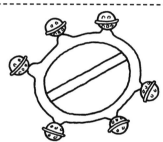 bells
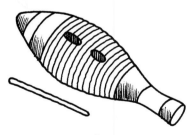 guiro	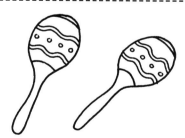 maracas	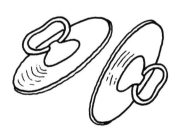 cymbals
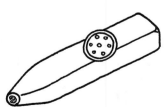 kazoo	 cabasa	 tabla

Teachers' note The children first need an opportunity to explore the ways in which they can produce sounds using musical instruments. Ask them what they need to do with the instrument in order to make a sound. They can then group them in sets that produce sounds in the same way. Ask them to cut out the pictures on this page and to glue them into groups on another sheet of paper.

Developing Science
Year 1
© A & C BLACK

Sound bingo

Understand that we can make sounds in a variety of ways

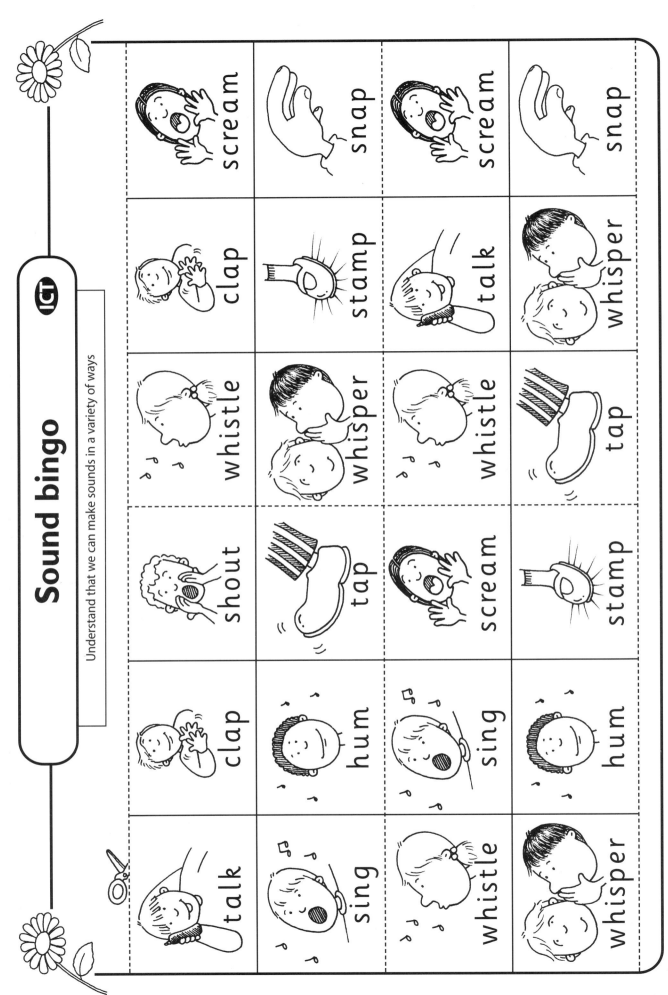

Teachers' note Ask the children to take turns to make a sound; ask the others to listen and name the sound. Introduce new words as necessary. This game is intended for four children. Copy the page and cut out the bingo cards along the dotted lines. Give a card to each child. Make one of the sounds; if a child's card has that sound, they cover it. The first to cover all their pictures wins.

Developing Science
Year 1
© A & C BLACK

Quiet and loud

Explore sounds using hearing

• **Sort the sounds:** | quiet | loud |

snore

beep

drill

drip

flush

swish

brush

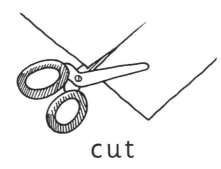

cut

slam

ring

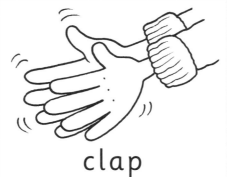

clap

rattle

Teachers' note Ask the children to be first as quiet and then as noisy as possible; talk about the different things they did to be quiet and noisy. Ask them about quiet and loud noises they hear at home and outdoors and what it is like to be close to the sources of these sounds. Talk about the words they know for sounds; introduce new words (see page 11).

Developing Science
Year 1
© A & C BLACK

Muffle it

- **Give your partner earmuffs.**
- **Make some sounds.**
- **Ask your partner to say what each sound is.**
- **Do it again without earmuffs.**

Which ones did they get right? ✔ or ✘	earmuffs	no earmuffs
triangle		
blow		
knock		
draw		

• **Write the sounds in order:**

quietest	⟶	loudest

Now try this!

Teachers' note The children should first have completed page 61. Remind them about their ideas of how to avoid loud noises and how people protect their ears from loud noises. What difference do they think earmuffs make? The children could work in groups; one listens (facing away from the others) while the others make sounds. They record whether or not he or she could identify the sounds with, and then without, earmuffs. Ask them if the earmuffs made a difference. How could they tell?

Developing Science
Year 1
© **A & C BLACK**

Far-off sounds: 1

Recognise that sounds change at different distances

Which sounds will you hear from:

| a long way off |
| a short way off |
| close up |

Sound	How far?
phone	_____ _____ _____
drawing	_____ _____ _____
bell	_____ _____ _____
talking	_____ _____ _____

How can you find out which sounds you can hear from far off?

Teachers' note The children should first have completed pages 61 and 62. Take them outside to listen to sounds. Can they identify any that come from a long way off? How do they know they are being made a long way off? (Can they see the sources?) Read this page with them and ask them to predict which sounds they will be able to hear at different distances. Ask them to explain their predictions. See also page 64.

Developing Science
Year 1
© A & C BLACK

Far-off sounds: 2

Communicate what happened using a chart

From how far off did you hear the sounds?

• Glue the pictures onto the chart.

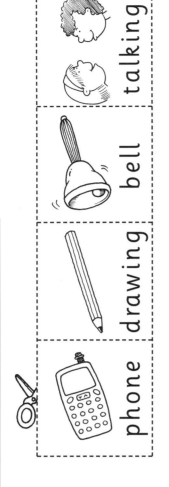

phone | drawing | bell | talking

close up ——→ a short way off ——→ a long way off

• Write the same sounds in order in the boxes.

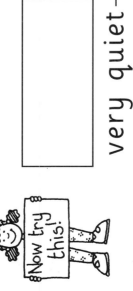

Now try this!

very quiet ——→ quiet ——→ in between ——→ loud

Teachers' note The children should first have completed pages 61–63. They could chalk marks on the playground to indicate the distances at which different sounds were heard. Discuss the results of the investigation and ask the children if their predictions were right. Why can some sounds be heard from farther off than others?

Developing Science
Year 1
© A & C BLACK